Bowman-

T4-AQK-046

WILLIAM D. SHELDON

QUEENIE B. MILLS

MARGARET K. MOORE

Our School

ALLYN AND BACON, INC.

BOSTON   ROCKLEIGH, N.J.   ATLANTA   DALLAS   BELMONT, CALIF.

SHELDON BASIC READING SERIES

Centennial Edition

ILLUSTRATED BY ELEANOR MILL, AL FIORENTINO
COVER ILLUSTRATIONS: NORMAN LALIBERTÉ

Library of Congress Catalog Card Number 68-19303

Contents

We Go to School

Pets At School

School Days

A Ride to the Farm

We Go to School

A Coat for School

The store man said, "Hi there.
Can I help you?"

Bill said, "I want a coat.
I want a coat for school."

"Blue?" said the man.

"Red!" said Bill.
"I want a red coat."

Jay said, "Look, Mother.
There is a school coat."

The store man said, "Hi there.
Let me help you."

"I want to get a coat," said Jay.
"Something for school.
I like that blue coat."

7

Bill said, "Hi, Jay.
What did you get?"

"A coat," said Jay.
"A blue coat for school.
My coat is like that coat.
What did you get?"

"A school coat," said Bill.
"My coat is not like that coat.
My coat is red."

8

Jay said, "Hi, Bill.
Is that you?
What coat did you get?"

Bill said, "The blue coat!
And I like it.
Did you get my red coat?"

"I did!" said Jay.
"And I like it!"

Good-by !

"Good-by, Ricky," said Bill.
"Away I go to school.
Good-by !   Good-by !"

"Good-by, Ricky," said Linda.
"Away I go to school, too.
Good-by! Good-by!"

Ricky looked down at Midnight.

"See that," said Ricky.
"That is my little yellow wagon.
Get in the wagon, Midnight.
Jump in and ride with me.
We will go to school, too."

Ricky looked up at Rags.
"You come too," said Ricky.

Rags did not like the wagon.
He did not want to ride in it.
So he did not go with Ricky.

"Good-by, Rags," said Ricky.
"Away we go to school.
Good-by! Good-by!"

The Play School

"No, Ricky, no!" said Mother.
"Come home, Ricky.
You can not go to school.
You are too little."

14

"Come, Midnight," said Ricky.

"We can not go to school.

We are too little.

We will go and play with Rags.

We can play school at home."

"My, my," said Mother.
"What is this I see?
Is it a little school?"

Ricky said, "Come in, Mother.
This is my play school.
Rags comes to this school.
Midnight comes to this school.
You can come to this school, too."

"Help ! Help !" said Mother.
"Down I go !"

"Mother, Mother," said Ricky.
"This is funny !
We can not go to school.
We are too little.
And you can not play school.
You are too big."

A Letter for Ricky

Bill said, "Ricky, look!
This is for you.
Come and get it."

"Run fast, Ricky," said Linda.
"It is something you will like."

18

"What is it?" said Ricky.
"I like cookies.
But it is not cookies.
I like ice cream.
But it is not ice cream.
What is it, Bill?"

Bill said, "Look and see.
It is a letter for you."

Ricky took the letter.
"Thank you," he said.

Ricky looked at the letter.
He looked and looked and looked.

"Bill! Bill!" said Linda.
"Look at Ricky.
He can not read the letter.
He is too little to read."

Bill said, "I can read.

I like to read.

Come here, Ricky.

I will read it to you."

This is what the letter said:

Dear Ricky,

Come to our school.

Come for a day.

Come and see our school.

Bill and Linda.

21

The Big Day

"Get up, Bill," said Ricky.

"This is the day I go to school
with you and Linda.

Get up fast, Bill.

This is the big day!"

"Ricky," said Bill.
"Get ready for school.
Linda and I are ready to go.
But you are not ready."

Ricky said, "I will get ready.
I can get ready fast."

"Look up, Bill," said Linda.

"Here comes Ricky.

He is all ready for school."

Bill looked up at Ricky.

"I see a ball, a boat, and a car,"
said Bill.

"What is all that?"

"All this will go to school
with me." said Ricky.

"I will take my red ball.
I will take my blue boat.
I will take my yellow car, too.
I will want all this at school."

"Come, Bill," said Linda.
"We can help.
This is a BIG DAY for Ricky."

Ricky Comes to School

"Here we are," said Bill.
"Look, Ricky.
This is our school."

"It is my school, too,"
said Ricky.

"Come, Ricky," said Bill
and Linda.

"Come and see our school."

"This is Mr. Works.
Mr. Works runs our school."

"This is Mr. Little.
He works at our school, too."

"This is our school nurse.
We like our nurse."

27

"What is in there?" said Ricky.
"It looks big to me."

Bill said, "It is big.
We play ball in there."

"Where are the balls?"
said Ricky.
"I want to play ball, too."

"Not now," said Bill.
"We can not play ball now."

28

"What is in here?" said Ricky.
"Can we get cookies in here?
Can we get ice cream, too?"

"Not now," said Bill.
"We can not stop now for cookies
and ice cream."

"Where are we now?" said Ricky.
"I like it in here."

"This is where I work," said Linda.
"Want to make some **A B C** letters?
Want to read a book?
Come with me and I will help you."

"Not now," said Ricky.
"I can read at home.
I want to play now."

And Ricky played and played
all that day at school.

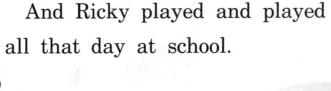

Pets at School

Yuki

Yuki sat up in bed.
But she did not get up.

"Are you up?"
said Yuki's mother.

"No, Mother," said Yuki.
"But I will get up now."
And up she jumped.

That day Yuki took something
to school.

She wanted to get there fast.

So she ran all the way.

It was a happy day for Yuki.

Near the school Yuki met
Bill and Jay.
She said, "Hi, Bill! Hi, Jay!
Come here and see my pet."

Bill and Jay ran to look.
"Where is it?" said Bill.

"Here it is," said Yuki.
"Look in my hand."

Bill and Jay did look.
There in Yuki's hand was
a little cage.

34

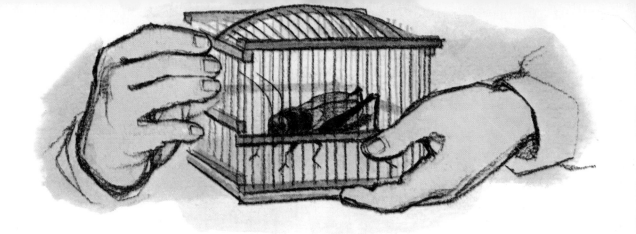

"Look in the cage," said Yuki.
"My little pet is in there."

Bill said, "I see it.
But it looks funny to me."

"It is not like our pets,"
said Jay.
"What is it, Yuki?"

"This is a cricket cage,"
said Yuki.
"And that is my pet cricket
in the cricket cage."

35

Little Red

One day Will took a pet
to school in a box.

It was a big box, too.

"Here comes Will with a pet,"
said Linda.

"What is it, Will?

What is in that big box?

Come in, come in.

We want to see the pet."

Something little and red
looked up at Linda.

It was a little red hen.

"This is Little Red Hen,"
said Will.

"Little Red Hen," said Linda.
"This is our school.
You will like our school.
We will make a cage for you."

The children did make a cage
for the little red hen.

Mr. Little helped the children.

"Little Red Hen," said Will.

"This is Mr. Little.

Mr. Little works at our school.

He likes our pets.

He helped to make this cage
for you."

One day Linda said, "Look!"

"Where?" said all the children.

"In Little Red Hen's cage,"
said Linda.
"I see something brown in there.
Can you see what I see?
Can you see something brown?"

"Here it is," said Will.
"One big brown egg!
Run and get Mr. Little, Linda.
He will want to see
the big brown egg, too.
Mr. Little helped
with Little Red's cage.
This egg is for Mr. Little!"

40

Something to See

"Bill and Linda! Come with me!"
said Miss Brown.

"There is something in here
I want you to see."

"Is it a hen in a box?" said Bill.
"Is it one brown egg?" said Linda.

Miss Brown looked at the children.
"Come with me, and you will see,"
she said.

"Where is it?" said Linda.
"All I can see in here
is our big white rabbit."

"Look in the rabbit's cage,"
said Miss Brown.

The children looked in the cage.
Bill said, "Now I see something.
Linda look! Little white rabbits!
Look at the little white rabbits!"

42

"Here comes Mr. Works,"
said Linda.

"He likes our big white rabbit.
He will want to see
the little white rabbits."

Mr. Works said, "Little rabbits!
Are there little rabbits in here?"

"Yes, there are," said Linda.
"Come and look."

"Here comes Miss Read,
the school nurse," said Bill.
   "She will want to see
the little white rabbits, too."

Miss Read said, "Little rabbits!
Are there little rabbits in here?"

"Yes, there are," said Bill.
"Come and look."

44

Mr. Works looked for the rabbits.
Miss Read looked, too.

"Where are the little rabbits?"
the nurse said.
"All we can see in here
is a little red hen."

Bill wanted to laugh.
Linda wanted to laugh, too.
But no one did laugh.

45

Bill said, "Look in this cage.
The little rabbits are here
in this cage."

Miss Read and Mr. Works looked
in the cage near Bill.

"Now I see the little rabbits,"
said Miss Read.

"Yes, yes," said Mr. Works.
"This is something to see !"

The Pet Store

"Look at our fish," said Jay.
"He wants something.
But look at this box!"

Miss Day looked at the box
in Jay's hand.
She said, "We can get that
at the pet store.
The pet store is near school.
So let's get ready and go now."

Miss Day took the children
to the pet store.

"Children, this is Mr. Car."
she said.

"Mr. Car," said Jay.
"We want a box like this one.
It is for our fish."

"I will get it for you,"
said Mr. Car.
"And you can look at my pets."

It was fun to see the pets.

It was fun for the children.

It was fun for Miss Day, too.

49

"Here is the box," said Mr. Car.
"And here is a pet
I want you to see.
This is Go Go, children.
Come and see my funny pet.
Come and see Go Go.
He wants to play with you."

50

Go Go was a funny little pet.
He made the children laugh.
He made Miss Day laugh, too.

"Go Go," said Miss Day.
"We can not play with you all day.
Our little fish is at school.
He will want what is in this box.
Come, children.
Let's get ready to go."

"Good-by, Mr. Car,"
said the children.
"This was fun. Thank you!
We liked all the pets
in the cages.
We liked Go Go, too.
Good-by, Go Go!"

Mr. Car said good-by.
Go Go said good-by, too.

52

We Want a Pet Show

The children wanted to have
a pet show.

"We will work and work,"
said Linda.
"All the children will help.
Will you help, Mr. Works?"

Mr. Works said, "Yes,
I will help.

A pet show will be fun."

Bill said, "Our pet show
will be a big show.

Where can we have it?"

Mr. Works said, "Come with me.
Let's go and look at the gym."

"Mr. Little," said Mr. Works.
"The children want to have
a pet show.
It will be big.
Where can we have a big show ?"

"This gym is big," said Mr. Little.
"The pet show can be in here."

All the children worked
to get ready for the pet show.

Mr. Little and Mr. Works helped.

Mr. Little helped to make
big cages for the big pets.

Mr. Works helped to make
little cages for the little pets.

"Work, work, work.

Fun, fun, fun.

Pet show day.

Come! Come! Come!"

said the children.

Mr. Big

"This is Mr. Big,"
said Mr. Little.
"He is my pet.
He wants to be in the pet show."

"Mr. Big!" said the children.
"This is funny!
Mr. Big and Mr. Little!"

58

"Big! Little! Big! Little!
Here I am! Here I am!"
said Mr. Big.

"Where is the show?
Where is the show?
Where is the show?"

The children laughed and
laughed at Mr. Big.

"Now, let's get to work,"
said Miss Day.

"No! No! No!" said Mr. Big.
"Come and play! Come and play!"

"No," said Bill. "Not now!
We have work to do now."

"Yes! Yes! Yes!" said Mr. Big.
"Come and play! Come and play!"

60

The children wanted to read.

Mr. Big wanted to have fun.

"Help! Help!" he said.

"Look at me! Look at me!

Do something! Do something!"

All the children looked up.

Bill jumped up and ran to Mr. Big.

"Here I come," he said.

"I will help you, Mr. Big."

"Funny! Funny! Funny!"
said Mr. Big.

"I am funny, I am."

"Yes, you are," said Bill.
"You don't want my help.
You want to have fun."

"Funny! Funny! Funny!"
said Mr. Big.

The Pet Show

It was the pet show day.
Big pets came to school.
Little pets came to school.
Mothers came and children came.
Jay's Dog was there.
So was Yuki's cricket.
Rags and Midnight came
to be in the show.
Ricky and Mother came
to see the show.

63

Mother and Ricky looked
at all the pets.

They looked at brown rabbits.

They looked at white rabbits.

They looked at red hens.

They looked at white hens.

They looked at red, blue, green,
and yellow fish.

64

"Look, Mother, look!" said Ricky.

"Look at the white kitten.

Look at the yellow kitten.

Look at the black kitten.

I like the little black kitten.

That little black kitten

looks like our Midnight."

Mother saw a pet she liked, too.
"Oh Ricky!" she said.
"Come and see this big black dog."

"I don't like that black dog,"
said Ricky.
"He is too big.
I like little pets.
Come away, Mother, come away."

"Funny! Funny! Funny!"
said a big green pet.

Ricky looked up.
"Oh Mother!" he said.
"Look at that big green hen!
It said that I was funny.
I am not funny! So there!"

"Oh Ricky," laughed Mother.
"That is not a green hen.
That is Mr. Big."

Where Is the Cricket?

The school children liked
the pet show.
So did the little children.
The mothers liked it, too.
And all the pets liked it.
That is, all but one!

No one saw Yuki's pet cricket
get away.

But it did.

"Where is my little cricket?"
said Yuki.

"She came to school with me
in the cricket cage.

Now she is not here.

Where are you, little cricket?"

The cricket was not far away.

Rags saw it.

Dog saw it, too.

They saw it and they played
with it.

That was fun for the dogs,
but not for the cricket.

Yuki said, "Stop it!
Don't do that!
You will kill my cricket."

The dogs did not kill
the cricket.
Bill and Linda and Jay came
to help Yuki.

Linda said, "Jay, you get Dog.
Bill, you get Rags.
I will get the cricket."
And that is what they did.

"Thank you," said Yuki.
She was happy.

"Mothers and children," said Bill.
"We are happy you are here.
We are happy that you came
to our pet show.
Now we have a prize for the one pet
you all liked.
That pet is funny Mr. Big!"

"Where is the show?
Where is the show?"
said happy Mr. Big.

72

School Days

The Box Train

Bill was not happy.

Will was not happy.

Jay was not happy.

They didn't want to run.

They didn't want to jump.

They didn't want to play ball.

"Let's make something," said Jay.

"With what ?" said Bill.

74

Will said, "Oh, oh, look there.
Do you see what I see ?"

"Yes, I do !" said Bill.
"I see a little box.
I see a big box, too.
And one big, big box."

"Let's go !" said Jay.
"Now we can make something."

"What can we make ?" said Will.

"A train !" said Bill.
"Let's make a box train.
Help me, Will. Help me, Jay.
We will make a box train.
And all the children can ride
in it."

Bill and Will and Jay worked
to make the train.

A big boy and a big girl
came to help.

A little boy and a little girl
came to help, too.

A black dog and a white kitten
came to look.

The box train was ready !
The boys and girls wanted
to ride in it.

"Jump in," said Bill.
"We will all go for a ride
in our box train."

The black dog and the white kitten
wanted to ride in it, too.
Will laughed and said,
"Jump in."
And they did !

New Books

Linda came to school
with a new book.
It was a book she liked.
She wanted to show it
to the children.

"Hello, Will," said Linda.
"What do you have there?"

"My new book," said Will.
"I want to show it
to the children."

"Two new books!" said Linda.
"Miss Brown will be happy.
She likes new books."

"Hello, Linda! Hello, Will!"
said the children.

"What do you have there?"

"I have a book," said Linda.

"I have a book, too," said Will.

"Two new books in one day!"
said the children.

"Miss Brown will be happy.
She likes new books."

"Hello, Miss Brown, hello,"
said the children.
"What do you have there?"

"I have a new book for you,"
said Miss Brown.

The children laughed.
"Three new books!" they said.
"One, two, three new books
in one day!"

"Show the three new books !"
said the children.

"Here is my book," said Linda.
"It is **The Little Train**."

"Here is my book," said Will.
"It is **The Little Train**, too."

"And here is my book,"
laughed Miss Brown.
The children laughed, too.
The book was **The Little Train**.
"Three new books," they said.
"One, two, three **Little Trains** !"

Work and Play

It was a day for work and play.

Some children made boats.

Some children made cars.

Some children looked at books.

Some children played
in the play house.

"Miss Day! Miss Day!" said Bill.
"Come and see the boat I made.
And look at that car Jay made."

Miss Day came and looked.
She liked the boat Bill made.
She liked Jay's car, too.
"Good work, boys!" she said.

Yuki said, "Oh, Miss Day.
Did you read this book?
It's a pet book. See?
And it's a good one, too.
See the dogs and kittens.
See the rabbits and hens.
See all the fish."

Miss Day looked at the book.
She said, "I like it, too, Yuki.
It's a good one for you to read."

"Miss Day! Oh, Miss Day!"
said two little girls.

"Come to our play party!
It will be in the play house.
Will you come?"

Miss Day thanked the girls.
"Yes, thank you," she said.
"I will come to the party."

87

Mr. Works came to look
for Miss Day.

"Hello, boys and girls,"
he said.

"Where is Miss Day ?"

"Miss Day is at the party,"
said Bill.

"A party !" said Mr. Works.
"What party ?"

"Go and look in the play house,"
said Bill.

Mr. Works went to the play house.
There was the party!
And there was Miss Day!
The party looked like good fun.
So Mr. Works went to the party,
too.

Red Paint

There was a new store
near the school.

The children liked to stop
to look at it.

One day Bill said, "Oh, Linda.
Look at the new store now.
There is red paint on it.
The new store will be red.
I like red paint on stores."

"So do I," said Linda.
"But now we will have to run
to get to school."
And away they went.

91

Near the school,

Bill and Linda saw Will.

"Hello, you two," said Will.

"You look funny!

You look all red and funny.

What makes you look so red ?

Do you have colds ?"

Bill looked at Linda.

Linda looked at Bill.

They laughed at what they saw.

"No," they said.

"We don't have colds.

But we do look funny."

Will said, "Run to the nurse.

She will want to see you."

The school nurse looked at Bill.
She looked at Linda, too.
She laughed at what she saw.
"My, my," she said.
"You do look a little funny."

Linda said, "We don't have colds.
But we do have something.
What is it, Miss Read?
What do we have?
Will we have to go home?"

"No," laughed Miss Read.
"You won't have to go home.
That is red paint on you."

Bill said, "Yes! Yes! Yes!
I see what it is now.
It's that red store paint."

"This is funny," said Linda.
"We don't have colds.
We have RED PAINT!"

The Surprise

One day Jay came to school with a white box.

"What is in the white box?" said the children.

"I have a surprise," said Jay. "It's a surprise for Miss Day."

"Good!" said the children. "Surprises are fun."

In came Miss Day.

She saw the children at work.

But she didn't see the box.

So she sat down on it.

What a surprise!

"Miss Day! Miss Day!"
said the children.

"You are on the surprise!"

"That box is for you, Miss Day,"
said Jay.

"It's something I made at home.
My mother helped me.
It was a good surprise.
But it's not so good now."

Miss Day said, "Thank you, Jay.
But what is the surprise ?"

"Look in the box," said Jay.
"The surprise is in that box."

Miss Day looked in the box.
What she saw was cookies.
"Oh, Jay! Cookies!" she said.
"What a good surprise this is.
Thank you, Jay, thank you."

Jay was not happy.
"Look at my cookies," he said.
"I made big cookies.
Now they look little and funny."

"Jay," said Miss Day.
"I like my surprise."

"So do we !" said the children.

Miss Day laughed.
"We all like cookies," she said.
"So let's have a cookie party."

"That will be fun," said Jay.
And it was fun.
The children liked the cookie party.
They liked the cookies, too.

Lunch at School

"Hello, Bill," said Will.
"Come and eat lunch with me.
I have something good to eat
in my lunch box."

Bill said, "I have something good
in my lunch box, too."

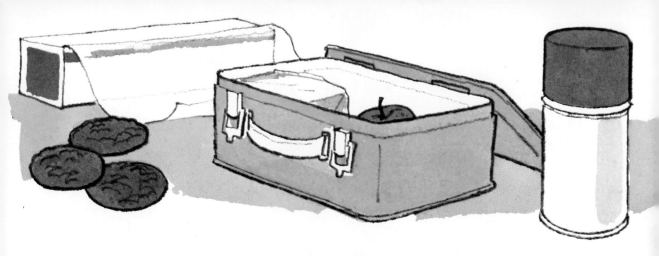

Will said, "My mother made
some brown cookies.

She put three big brown cookies
in my lunch box."

Bill said, "My mother made
some good yellow cake.

She put some yellow cake
in my lunch box."

"Look here !" said Will.

"This is not my lunch box.

There is yellow cake in this box.

Where is my lunch box ?"

"And this is not my lunch box,"
said Bill.

"There are three big brown cookies
in this box.

Where is my lunch box ?"

Will laughed and said, "Bill!
I have your yellow cake.
And you have my brown cookies!"

"That's it!" laughed Bill.
"I have your blue lunch box.
And you have my blue lunch box."

Will said, "I will eat my lunch.
Then I will paint **Will**
on my blue lunch box."

"That's good !" said Bill.
"I will eat my lunch now, too.
Then I will paint **Bill**
on my blue lunch box."

And that's what they did.

Two Surprises Today

"I painted something
at school today," said Linda.
"It is for Daddy.
I will put it up here.
Then Daddy will see it.
It will be a surprise."

"That will be fun," said Ricky.
"Daddy likes surprises."

106

"Look, Ricky," said Linda.
"My surprise is ready for Daddy.
Do you like what I painted?"

"Yes, I do," said Ricky.
"I like your big green tree.
I like your white rabbit.
I like your three kittens, too."

"Thank you, Ricky," said Linda.
Then away she went to play.

"I will paint something, too,"
said Ricky.

"The trees will be black.

Something will be green.

Something will be red and blue
and yellow, too.

Then there will be two surprises.

Daddy will be happy today."

Daddy came home.

"Daddy! Daddy!" said Linda.
"We have two surprises for you.
I painted one at school today.
Ricky painted one at home.
Come and see the one I painted."

"Look at this one," said Ricky.
"I painted this one.
See the black, black trees.
See the green, green rabbits.
See the red, blue, and yellow
kittens."

"My, my," laughed Daddy.
"Two good surprises today!
Thank you, Linda and Ricky.
Thank you! Thank you!"

A Book for Kate

"Kate, look here !" said Jay.
"I have a new book for you.
It's about a funny big fish.
Come and I will read it to you."

Kate came and Jay read.
Kate laughed and laughed.
Then she said, "Read !   Read !"

"I did read it," said Jay.
"Now I want to go and play."

Kate took the book to Mother.
"Read ! Read !" said little Kate.

"Come on, Kate," laughed Mother.
"I will read your book to you."

Kate came and Mother read.
"Now run and play," said Mother.

Kate didn't want to play then.
She wanted to hear some one read
about the funny fish.

Kate ran to look for Daddy.
"Read! Read!" she said.

Daddy read the book to Kate.
Then he said, "Now, Kate.
I have to stop and go to work."

"Read! Read!" said little Kate.

"Not today!" laughed Daddy.
"Now you run and play with Dog."

Kate took the book and went
to look for Dog.

113

Two days went by.

"Where is my book ?" said Jay.

"The one about the funny fish.

I have to take it to school

today."

"Look there !" said Jay's mother.

Jay looked at Kate and laughed.

"Kate likes that book," he said.

"Let's get one like it

for our little Kate."

114

A Ride to the Farm

Come to My Farm

Mary was a new girl at school.

One day she said, "My home is on a farm.

Will you come to see our farm?

I want you to see my pets."

"Yes! Yes!" said the children.

"We will come to see your farm."

What To Do.
1. Ask Mr. Works.
2. Ask our Mothers.
3. Ask for the school bus.

One boy said,
"We will have to ask Mr. Works."

One girl said,
"We will have to ask our Mothers."

Then Mary said,
"Our farm is not near school.
    You will have to come
in the school bus."

Some children went
to see Mr. Works.
"Hello, Mr. Works," they said.
"We want to ask you something.
We want to see a farm.
May we go to see a farm?"

"Yes, you may," said Mr. Works.
"Farms are fun to see."

118

Some children went
to see Mr. Downs.

"Hello, Mr. Downs," they said.

"We want to ask you something.

We want to go to a farm.

May we go in your bus?"

"Yes, you may," said Mr. Downs.

"You may go in the school bus.

And I will go with you."

The children took letters home
about Mary's farm.

"Mother !   Mother !" they said.

"We want to go to a farm.

We want to go on the school bus.

Read the letter !

May we go ?"

"Yes," said all the mothers.

"You may go to the farm.

You may go on the school bus."

The Bus Ride

It was the day to go
to the farm.

"Jump in the bus,"
said Mr. Downs.
"I am ready to go now."

In jumped the children.
And away went the bus.

The children saw big cars
and little cars.
They saw big stores
and little stores.
They saw big houses
and little houses.

On and on
went the big yellow bus.
On and on it went.
And it did not stop.

Soon the children
did not see the cars.

They did not see the stores.

They did not see the houses.

They saw green, green trees.

But the big yellow bus
did not stop.

On and on it went.

124

"Mr. Downs ! Mr. Downs !"
said the children.
"Where is the farm ?
Are we near it ?
Will we get there soon ?"

Mr. Downs laughed.
"We are there now !" he said.
"Now I will stop the bus."
And he did.

Little Lamb

Mary saw the big yellow bus.
Mary's daddy saw it, too.
And so did Mary's mother.

"Here they come!" said Mary.
"Here come the children
to see our farm!"

126

"Hello, Mary, hello,"
said all the children.
"Here we are!
We have come to see your farm.
We have come to see your pets."

127

A little white lamb
came to look.

It was Mary's little lamb.

It saw the big bus stop.

Then it saw the children get out.

The little white lamb looked
at the big yellow bus.

It looked at all the children.

Then it ran away.

It ran away fast!

The lamb hid in the dog house.
It looked out at the girls.
It looked out at the boys.
But it did not come out.

"Come out, Little Lamb,"
said Mary.
"I have something for you.
Come out and get it."

Mary had something
for Little Lamb to eat.

It was something he liked.

So Little Lamb came out
to get it.

Mary said, "Come and play
with my Little Lamb.

He is out now.

Now he will play with you."

Soon Little Lamb did play
with the children.

The little lamb had fun.

The children had fun, too.

Mary's daddy laughed.

"You boys and girls have
a new friend," he said.

"Yes," said the boys and girls.

"Little Lamb is our good friend
now."

Happy the Farm Dog

"This is Happy," said Mary.

"Happy is our farm dog.

He helps Daddy do the farm work."

"What can Happy do?" asked Bill.

"Come to the barn," said Mary.

"I will show you

what Happy can do."

The children ran to the barn.
Then Mary said, "Go, Happy, go!
Go and get the cows.
Put the cows in the barn."

Away ran Happy to get the cows.
He made the cows go
to the barn.

Then Mary said, "Go, Happy, go!
Go and get the ducks.
Go and get the hens, too.
Put the ducks in the barn.
Put the hens in the hen house."

Away ran Happy.
He made the ducks run
to the barn.
He made the hens run
to the hen house.

134

"You are a good dog," said Mary.
"Now you may play
with my friends."

All Mary's friends played
with Happy.
All but Bill!
Bill saw a rabbit near a tree.
He ran to look at the rabbit.

Soon Linda said, "Where is Bill?
He is not here.
Did he go into the barn?"

The children went into the barn
to look for Bill.
They saw the cows.
They saw the ducks.
But they didn't see Bill.

Then into the barn
ran Bill and Happy.

"Here I am!" laughed Bill.

"Happy came to get me.

He made me run to the barn."

"Happy is a good farm dog,"
laughed the children.

"He can go and get the cows.

He can go and get the ducks.

He can go and get the hens.

He can go and get children, too!"

Big Black

"That's Big Black," said Mary.
"Big Black is our funny horse.
He eats and eats and eats!"

Mary's daddy laughed.
"Come, Big Black," he said.
"You have had your lunch.
Now you have work to do.
Mary's friends want to ride you."

"May I ride ?" asked Bill.

"May I ride ?" asked Jay.

"May I ride, too ?" asked Will.

Mary's daddy laughed.
"Yes, you may," he said.
"Big Black is a big horse.
Three can ride on Big Black."

Mary's daddy put all three boys
on the big black horse.

"Run, Big Black, run,"
said Bill.
"Run to that tree."

Big Black ran.

But he didn't run to the tree.

He ran to the barn.

"Stop, Big Black, stop !"
said Bill.

But the big horse didn't stop.

He ran into the barn.

Then Big Black did stop.
He wanted to eat!

Bill and Jay and Will
laughed and laughed.
"Big Black is a funny horse,"
they said.
"He eats and eats and eats."

The Egg Game

Mary's daddy had a red box
and a blue box.

He said, "Look, boys and girls.

See what I have.

The red box is for the boys.

The blue box is for the girls.

Now we will have some fun.

We will play the egg game.

Who wants to play?"

"The egg game!" said Bill.
"What is the egg game?"

Mary's daddy laughed and said,
"The game is to find eggs.
Run and get all the eggs
that you can find.
Put the eggs in your box.
Then run here to me."

144

Bill said, "Come on, boys.

We will go to the hen house.

We can find eggs in there."

The boys did find eggs

in the hen house.

One, two, three big eggs!

They put the three big eggs

in the red box.

Then they ran to Mary's daddy.

Linda said, "Come on, girls.
I saw the boys go
to the hen house.
We will go to the barn."

The girls ran to the barn.
They looked and looked for eggs.
They didn't find eggs.
But they did find something
to put in the blue box.

"Look in our box," said the boys.

"Good !" said Mary's daddy.
"You boys did find some eggs.
I see one, two, three big eggs."

"Look in our box," said the girls.

"Oh ! Oh !" said Mary's daddy.
"You girls didn't find eggs today.
But you did find something.
I see one, two, three
little kittens !"

The New Friend

Little Lamb wanted to play
with the children.

But the children wanted
to play games.

Little Lamb didn't like games.

So he ran away.

Little Lamb ran to the barn.

He wanted to play with Happy.

But Happy had work to do.

He had to go and find the cows.

Little Lamb wanted to play

with Big Black.

But the funny big horse

didn't want to play.

He wanted to eat.

149

Little Lamb saw a rabbit.

He ran to play with the rabbit.

But the rabbit ran away.

Little Lamb saw a duck.

He ran to play with the duck.

But the duck ran into the barn.

Little Lamb saw a kitten.

He ran to play with the kitten.

But the kitten ran up a tree.

Little Lamb was not happy.
He was not happy at all!
He had no one to play with.

Then Little Lamb looked down.
He saw something funny.
It looked like
a little black lamb.

Little Lamb jumped up and down.
The little black lamb
jumped up and down, too.

Then Little Lamb ran fast.
And the little black lamb
ran fast, too.

Little Lamb was happy, now.
He had a new friend!

The Surprise Cakes

"Lunch is ready!" said Mary.

"That's good!" said Bill.

"I am ready to eat."

"So am I!" said Linda.

"So are we!"
said all the boys and girls.
Then they ran to have lunch.

153

The children had a good lunch.
Then Mary's mother came out
with something they all liked.
It was cold, cold ice cream
and little party cakes.

Mary said, "The little cakes
are surprise cakes."

"What are surprise cakes ?"
asked Bill.

Mary laughed and said,
"Eat one and you will find out."

Soon Bill said, "I see something
in my little cake!
It's a funny little dog.
And it looks like Rags!"
"Oh, look!" said Linda.
"I have a funny little kitten.
And it looks like Midnight."

"Yes," laughed Mary.
"Mother put surprises
in all the little cakes."

Then all the children looked
to find the surprises.

Some little cakes had ducks.
Some little cakes had hens.
Some little cakes had cows
and some had horses.
Some little cakes had rabbits
and some had lambs.

One little cake had a ball in it.
Two little cakes had trains.
And three had funny fish.

Soon Mr. Downs came
with the big yellow bus.

"Get ready to go home," he said.

"Good-by, Mary, good-by,"
said all the children.

"We had fun at your farm today.
Good-by and thank you!"

Then the children jumped
into the big yellow school bus.

And away they went.

Our School

Basic Words: 87   *Phonic Sets Words:* 19   *Enrichment Words:* 4
Cumulative Vocabulary (Basic and Phonic Sets Words): 196

Our School is designed to be read after successful completion of *Here and Away.*

The 110 words introduced in *Our School* are listed below in the order of their introduction. They are of three major types:

Basic Words: Words which will appear repeatedly but which most children will be unable to identify independently. They include basic vocabulary units which will be used to develop word-analysis skills and frequently used irregular words which should be taught as wholes.

Phonic Sets Words (PS): A phonic set is a group of new words derived phonically from a known basic word by substitution or addition of initial consonants, consonant blends, or consonant digraphs. **Phonic Sets Words** in this book are limited to initial consonant substitution. Children are expected to use their developing word-analysis skills to identify these new **(PS)** words.

Enrichment Words (E): Interesting meaningful words which have limited use at this level but which are needed at times to improve readability and story comprehension. They are words often unsuited to analysis but easily recognized because they appear in obvious context and are carefully illustrated.

Variants formed by adding *'s* or *s* and *ed* or *d* to known roots are not listed as new words. Words formed by the subtraction of such endings are also not listed as new.

5. school	12. wagon (E)	20. read
6. coat (PS)	13. so (PS)	21. dear (PS)
store	14. are	day (PS)
7. like	15.	22.
8. what	16. this	23. ready
9.	17.	24. all
10. good-by	18. letter	25.
11. too	19. but	26.

158

27. Mr.
    nurse
28. where
    now
29.
30. books (PS)
31. pets
32. Yuki
    sat (PS)
    bed (PS)
    she
33. way (PS)
    was
34. met (PS)
    hand (PS)
    cage
35. cricket (E)
36. one
    box
37. hen
38. children
39. brown
40. egg
41. Miss
42. white
    rabbit
43. yes
44.
45. laugh
46.
47. let's
48.
49.

50.
51. made
52.
53. show
    have
54. be (PS)
    gym (E)
55.
56.
57.
58.
59. am
60. do
61.
62. don't
63. came
64. they
65. kitten
    black
66. Oh
67.
68.
69. saw
70. far (PS)
71. kill (PS)
72. prize (E)
73.
74. train
    didn't
75.
76.
77. boy
    girl

78.
79. new
80. hello
    two
81.
82. three
83.
84. house
85. good
86. it's
87. party
88.
89. went
90. paint
91. on
92. colds
93.
94.
95. won't (PS)
96. surprise
97.
98.
99.
100.
101. lunch
    eat
102. put
    cake (PS)
103.
104. your
    that's
105. then
106. today

72 73 ST 9 8 7 6 5 4

160